Telemedicine

A Practical Guide for Professionals

Andrea Kamenca, MBA

MINDVIEW PRESS

Phoenix, Arizona

To my father who taught me to seek more,
To my mother who encouraged me to learn,
And, to my beloved partner, husband, and friend,
Thank you.

Table of Contents

Author's Note

The purpose of this book is to provide you, the professional, an implementation guide that is firmly rooted in telemedicine's core concepts. This guide defines and addresses key aspects of telemedicine, while suggesting an approach to adopt telemedicine in your organization.

I entered the healthcare field by working for a specialized public health clinic. During that time, a respected healthcare leader introduced me to telemedicine. I spent the next four years implementing a host of telemedicine projects for multiple organizations. I discovered that although many people had heard of telemedicine, there were significant knowledge gaps, especially in complex aspects of achieving operational success.

I wrote this book as a concise overview of telemedicine and the complexities associated with its implementation. This is not a comprehensive textbook nor is it meant to be an exhaustive discussion about the merits of telemedicine. Telemedicine has tremendous promise to make our health system more personal and effective. It is more likely to be successful when a devoted team thoughtfully and consistently addresses the organizational and operational details required to make the projects work. Telemedicine's promise can only be realized when a commitment is made to change the organization's operational systems so that telemedicine services can be planned, piloted, launched, and scaled.

Healthcare professionals are busy. It is tough to get "mind share" for innovation. It is especially difficult to make a case for new delivery methods, like telemedicine, that may or may not include incremental revenue. Most organizations use a technology purchase to prompt the discussion or force a pilot project. Yet, often these pilot projects are unsustainable or unable to scale due to the significant operational processes not addressed during the pilot.

As previously mentioned, this book is a brief guide. My goal was to provide enough information such that a person can read the book at one sitting or simply use it as a resource. The appendix is rich with links to additional resources including organizations to join, mailing lists to subscribe, and other resources to build your knowledge base and your program.

If you have any comments, feel free to send me an email at andrea.innovia@gmail.com. Thanks for reading!
Andrea

Part 1 Telemedicine Foundations

Chapter 1

Telemedicine Then and Now

What is Telemedicine?

Telemedicine refers to the delivery of healthcare services via an electronic device. Examples include continuous monitoring of patients in a hospital, a consumer accessing a physician over a web camera at home for a diagnosis and a potential pharmaceutical treatment, and even the movement of images to access specialized radiologists for diagnosis.

Telehealth is a broader term that includes not only the means of providing medical care and consultations but also includes education and training delivered using technology and communication systems. In the broadest terms, it is the exchange of medical information from one site to another via electronic communications to provide patient care, treatment, and services.

Telemedicine Then

In the beginning, rural areas used telemedicine to gain specialized physician services. Typically, they would install a complex and proprietary communications system and then strike an agreement with an urban hospital. The rural hospital physician in an emergency room, for example, would contact a stroke neurologist in a nearby urban center using those proprietary systems when potential stroke patients arrived in the emergency department.

Considered a tool for the rural areas, telemedicine funding was distributed by federal government agencies like the Department of Agriculture and the Federal Communications Commission, not Department of Health and Human Services, as one might expect. The proprietary systems and regional telemedicine resource centers were primarily grant funded and the ability to bill for telemedicine health services delivered was dependent upon a rural geography.

Telemedicine Now

Now, broadband and cellular access is ubiquitous. People are comfortable with technology. The dynamic nature of today's healthcare environment is forcing practitioners, healthcare systems, administrators, and patients to seek new, more effective care delivery methods even in urban settings. The explosive growth in the retail clinics located inside pharmacies from 2010 to 2017 is proof that the average patient as a consumer is willing to seek care in alternative settings. At the same time, payment for medical services is shifting from fee-for-service based models to population health management. Telemedicine as a delivery tool not only manages population health and offers convenience to low acuity patients, it also has the ability to monitor medically complex patients, create new revenue sources, and shift the care continuum.

Telemedicine Challenges

Still, there are challenges surrounding telemedicine's use. Key challenges include complicated billing, cross-state licensure, state laws that vary regarding the definition of a medical exam, malpractice insurance, and a lack of trained people to implement complex telemedicine programs. Yet, with all the challenges, telemedicine is growing exponentially. Hundreds of successful telemedicine implementations are making a positive difference for patients. There are estimates that telehealth use in the urgent care space, alone, will double in the next two years.[1]

---

[1] http://www.hhnmag.com/articles/8350-telehealth-adoption-to-double-by-2018&

Chapter 2

Trends Creating Telemedicine Opportunities

A "perfect storm" of trends is pressuring existing healthcare delivery methods to change. These trends include rising medical costs, an aging population, extended life spans, an increase in complex chronic conditions, and consumerism. Below is a brief overview of these trends and others that are boosting telemedicine's growth.

Technology

The American Recovery and Reinvestment Act and the Health Information Technology for Economic and Clinical Health Act (HITECH Act) of 2009 offered significant incentives for hospitals to implement electronic health records (EHRs). As this tremendous shift occurred, healthcare embarked upon a new path to technology-based systems. Healthcare has been a "laggard" industry in terms of its technology adoption but the EHR implementations opened the door for additional technology solutions. The new emphasis on technology has transformed large health systems and has dramatically increased the number of technological experts who are available to assist with technology adoption.

Accountability in the Acute Care Environment

The Affordable Care Act (ACA) and healthcare payment trends encouraged new payment models that emphasized prevention, population health and a wider view of healthcare delivery. The US Government, the nation's largest medical cost payer, pays 64% of the bills related to healthcare. [2] Medicare and Medicaid have paid a "fee for service" for hospital stays and procedures. Consequently, hospital costs have dramatically escalated. Medicare is trying to drive down acute care costs and is making acute environments more accountable for outcomes.

For example, Medicare withholds payment[3] for patients who after an initial hospitalization are re-hospitalized within 30 days. At the same time, Medicare is working to align patient acuity more closely with the appropriate care setting. They are using financial pressure to shift payment from acute care to the post-acute environment.

Population Health Management, New Payment Models, and the Triple Aim

One of telemedicine's key drivers is the shift to population health management. Accountable care organizations, health maintenance organizations and others are exploring strategies

---

[2] http://www.pnhp.org/news/2016/january/government-funds-nearly-two-thirds-of-us-health-care-costs-american-journal-of-pub

[3] https://www.cms.gov/medicare/medicare-fee-for-service-payment/acuteinpatientpps/readmissions-reduction-program.html

to limit medical care consumption by keeping patients healthy and encouraging the appropriate care setting for their ailment. Population health management is changing how and where healthcare is delivered.

Telemedicine delivers health care in new settings like a patient's home; sites that are much more affordable than the emergency department or inpatient facilities. To that end, telemedicine assists population health managers by driving down the cost of care. It offers a way to manage patients outside of the traditional care continuum thereby, saving costs and often, improving outcomes.

All of the recent changes in payment, a shift to the non-acute setting, and quality measures have prompted organizations to develop a "Triple Aim" of the targeted improvements. Developed by Don Berwick, Tom Nolan, and John Wittington[4], the Triple Aim measures a population's overall health, the individual patient's experience of care and, the per capita cost of care. The Triple Aim's goal is to improve a patient's health whilst the patient's care experience is good and costs decrease. The Institute for Healthcare Improvement (IHI)[5], the US National Quality Strategy, and other organizations around the world have adopted the Triple Aim as a comprehensive goal for health systems.

---

[4]http://www.ihi.org/resources/Pages/IHIWhitePapers/AGuidetoMeasuringTripleAim.aspx

[5] http://www.ihi.org/Topics/TripleAim/Pages/default.aspx

Aging Population Living Longer with Chronic Conditions

The baby boom population is the largest population in the United States. Born between 1944 and 1964 more than 10,000 people every day turn 65 years of age and are therefore are eligible for Medicare. In 1960, only 9% of the population was older than 65. By 2030, 21% of the population will be greater than 65 years of age.[6] In addition, they are living far longer than previous generations. Between 1900 and 1994, life expectancy for the average American increased from about 47 to 76 years of age. From 1965, when Medicare was created, the average life expectancy increased nearly three full years.[7]

Chronic conditions are common among an aging population. Most Americans are prescribed two or more medications for chronic conditions.[8] As people age, chronic conditions get more complex and increase in number. Therefore, telemedicine tools like remote patient monitoring offer realistic and affordable solutions that successfully manage a population that is aging, living longer, and has multiple chronic complex conditions.

---

[6] http://www.prb.org/pdf16/aging-us-population-bulletin.pdf

[7] https://www.ssa.gov/history/pdf/ThirtyYearsPopulation.pdf

[8] https://www.cdc.gov/chronicdisease/about/multiple-chronic.htm

Emergency Room Use as Primary Care

Because EMTALA requires that people are treated in the emergency department regardless of their ability to pay, emergency departments are sometimes overused by people who need a primary care appointment or mental health services. Emergency departments, initially established to treat traumatic and emergent situations, are bursting at the seams. Estimates are that 71% emergency room care is unnecessary or avoidable. [9] Using telemedicine, especially telepsychiatry in the emergency department, is a viable approach to alleviate emergency room crowding.

Fewer Primary Care Physicians

The number of primary care physicians has steadily decreased over the years, increasing the burden on active family care practitioners. To be successful, a family practitioner must see 20 to 24 patients per day.[10] Operating above capacity, a typical family practice may not be able to see a patient for three weeks or more. These conditions limit patients' options for managing chronic diseases, low-acuity injuries or nuisance illnesses like colds and flu. Telemedicine is being used to treat low acuity patients and is a viable alternative for a patient who cannot schedule a provider appointment.

---

[9] http://www.beckershospitalreview.com/patient-flow/study-71-of-ed-visits-unnecessary-avoidable.html

[10] https://www.washingtonpost.com/news/to-your-health/wp/2014/05/22/how-many-patients-should-your-doctor-see-each-day/?utm_term=.6c256db64ded

18

Patients Less Likely to Have a Primary Care Physician

Millennials, a young more technologically astute population, visit a variety of healthcare providers, reversing the trend of the primary care physician as the center of a family or patient's care. It is estimated that 17-42% of patients are "un-doctored," meaning they do not have a primary care physician who manages their care.[11] In addition, they are more likely to see a doctor over a web camera whether or not they acknowledge a relationship with a family care provider. Particularly for young mothers, telemedicine is a convenient alternative to piling children into a vehicle and waiting in a doctor's office.

Patient as Consumer

Burdened with increased financial responsibility for their health care, the patient is acting more like a consumer with choices and less like a patient who is provided care. A consumer today is more likely to choose a doctor or hospital due to convenience, speed, or cost, almost as if they would choose a restaurant.

---

[11] http://www.fiercehealthcare.com/practices/many-americans-don-t-have-a-primary-care-doctor

The retail pharmacies are capitalizing on this trend. [12] The retail pharmacies discovered that patients were increasingly seeking care outside of the "normal" office hours physicians were keeping. They turned their brands and locations into more than just "drug stores" and built pharmacies with embedded clinics on nearly every urban corner staffed by mid-level providers like nurse practitioners and physician assistants. They are providing consumers with a lower-cost alternative to the primary care physician or urgent care.

Extending Specialists

As mentioned earlier, specialists reside primarily in urban areas.[13] Telemedicine enables patients in rural areas to access those specialists. Yet, even urban doctors may cover multiple acute care facilities in any one given day. Rather than the doctor travelling throughout the city, telemedicine is used to conduct an initial consultation to determine if a specialist needs to drive and lay hands on the patient.

[12]https://www.forbes.com/sites/greatspeculations/2015/08/28/walgreens -steps-up-retail-clinic-expansion-as-demand-for-convenient-care- grows/#3faab147141chttp://www.drugchannels.net/2017/02/retail-clinic- check-up-cvs-retrenches.html

[13]https://www.ncbi.nlm.nih.gov/pmc/articles/PMC1071163/

Technology Comfort

As patients become increasingly comfortable using technology[14], cell phone use improves, and broadband access is available, there are lower barriers to using technology in order to deliver and receive medical care.

Telemedicine offers solutions to address more than a dozen trends in healthcare. Telemedicine enables providers to deliver specialty care to patients regardless of location, assist with chronic disease management, provide continuous monitoring of in-hospital, rural, or home bound patients, and improves the patient experience by offering convenience, connection, and access to care. Patients benefit due to the convenience, reduced cost, and improved care. Telemedicine has great promise.

---

[14] http://www.pewresearch.org/fact-tank/2016/07/12/28-of-americans-are-strong-early-adopters-of-technology/

Chapter 3

Telemedicine Concepts and Definitions

Telemedicine offers myriad applications and uses. Like most unique and complex fields, telemedicine has developed a lexicon of terms. Although there are countless terms that may apply to telemedicine, this section reviews the most common.

Terms that sometimes used interchangeably are Telehealth and telemedicine. Yet, there is a distinct difference between the two terms. Specifically, telehealth is the exchange of medical information between one site and another with the objective to provide medical care, consultation, or education using information technology. Telehealth is a broader term than telemedicine.

Telemedicine is a subset of telehealth. Specifically, the definition of telemedicine is medical care enabled by the use of information technology between a medical provider in one physical location and a medical provider or patient in another physical location.

Telemedicine includes patient monitoring. Patient monitoring can occur at the patient's home or in an acute setting, like the intensive care unit. The concept of patient monitoring includes continuous monitoring and remote patient monitoring. Continuous monitoring assesses a patient's condition by tracking the patient's medical data. Including continuous monitoring under the umbrella of telemedicine, means one must incorporate the viewing of a patient through a camera or other technology to assess their condition. One example is eICU, a Philips program that monitors patient's vitals and other medical data while the patient is in the ICU.

Whereas, remote patient monitoring includes the use of devices to track and report health conditions in an outpatient setting. Typically, remote patient monitoring occurs in the home of patients, with the medical data sent to their health care provider for review and follow up.

Identifying the type of telemedicine transaction is critical to billing for the service and defines the type of telemedicine encounter. The two types of telemedicine encounter are asynchronous, meaning not occurring at the same time and, synchronous, or occurring simultaneously in "real time." An asynchronous or "Store and Forward" example is a photo of a dermatological condition sent to a dermatologist for later assessment and diagnosis. A synchronous encounter, for example, is a video consultation between a patient in a rural emergency department and a stroke neurologist in an urban location.

Telemedicine programs between urban and rural areas have developed their own language. Sometimes called the Hub and Spoke arrangement, the "Hub" refers to a central location, usually in an urban area, where physician experts reside. The "Spoke sites" are rural or community hospitals that are served by the hub site. Another term for the "spoke site" is "distant site," whereas, the urban location is called the "originating site."

With the advent of mobile devices, telemedicine services delivered via mobile devices are sometimes labeled mHealth, eHealth, digital health, or virtual health. Most of these terms refer to the use of mobile technology and wireless devices to improve health outcomes, deliver healthcare services and health research. (HIMSS)

Chapter 4

Telemedicine Types and Categories

Telemedicine is more than a patient "seeing" a physician over a web camera. The definition is much broader. The first step in determining if telemedicine is right for your organization is deciding the type of telemedicine to pilot and explore. There are many distinctive types of telemedicine. Telemedicine service categories are roles of the people participating in the clinical interaction, services offered setting, and transaction timing. This chapter describes the various types of telemedicine services and its categories.

Provider to Provider (P2P)

A P2P consultation occurs between physicians or providers. The interaction can occur synchronously or asynchronously. For example, a surgeon consulting with an oncologist using a live video feed is a provider-to-provider telemedicine encounter. Another example is an emergency physician consulting with a specialist without the patient being present.

Provider to Consumer (P2C)

A provider to patient or provider to "consumer" encounter is a face-to-face encounter between a provider and a patient via a web camera, robot, cart, or other video technology. The encounter occurs regardless of patient location, acuity level, or payer and can occur synchronously or asynchronously. It also includes continuous monitoring of patients with a visual monitoring device like a camera that may occur in the Intensive care unit or NICU.

Provider to Provider to Consumer (P2P2C)

The provider to provider to consumer interaction involves a consultation between physicians or providers while incorporating the patient into the interaction. Examples include emergency room psychiatric consultation requested by emergency room physician with the psychiatrist evaluating the patient while present in the emergency department and a stroke neurologist examining the patient while the emergency room physician is present during the video encounter.

Training: Provider to Provider and Educator to Consumer

Telehealth versus telemedicine includes education and the dissemination of health information. Although this book does not elaborate on these types of encounters, these examples are valuable applications in the telehealth field. Telehealth offerings can include medical education (CME, Tumor Boards, ECHO Model), consumer health information (Patients Like Me, WebMD, Patient Portal, Self-Monitoring Devices), and consumer medical information (Diabetes Education, Wound Dressing, First Aid.)

Telemedicine Setting (Acute versus Ambulatory)

Another way to categorize telemedicine is to consider the setting in which it is utilized. Telemedicine can occur in the acute environment, like the emergency department, the intensive care unit, the neonatal ICU, or even in the surgical suite.

Alternatively, it can occur in the ambulatory, home, and skilled nursing setting. When considering telemedicine, it is important to consider the setting, as it affects the billing and operational details associated with delivering the care.

Synchronous versus Asynchronous

Categorizing types of telemedicine encounters as synchronous i.e. occurring at the same time or asynchronous, meaning there is a separation between the medical event and the diagnosis, is another method for categorizing telemedicine encounters.

Summary Chart

The chart illustrates telemedicine use-case examples and its categories.

Type of Telemedicine service	Type of telemedicine service	Setting	Synchronous /Asynchronous
ICU / NICU monitoring	Continuous Monitoring or Provider to Consumer	Acute	S
Telestroke Networks, Behavioral Health	Provider to provider to consumer	Acute, Ambulatory	S
Dermatology, Pathology	Provider to provider	Acute or Ambulatory	A
Internal medicine doctor discusses case with cardiologist	Provider to provider consults	Acute or Ambulatory	S
Tumor Boards, Grand Rounds, Project Echo	Medical Education	Acute or Ambulatory	S, A
Chronic Complex patient visits	Provider to existing patient	Ambulatory	S
Various companies including Teladoc, American Well, Doctor on Demand	Provider to new patient (on demand)	Ambulatory, Occupational Health	S
Post-Discharge CHF patients monitored	Home monitoring	Ambulatory	S
Radiology images read by radiologists	Image Sharing	Acute and Ambulatory	A

Part 2 Telemedicine Examples

Chapter 5

Prominent Uses of Telemedicine

Telestroke

Telestroke is the most prevalent and popular use of telemedicine. Stroke symptoms require immediate assessment and intervention. When an ischemic stroke is diagnosed within four hours of onset and a "clot busting" drug administered, the likelihood of permanent disability and death significantly diminishes. If there is not a neurologist on site, telestroke, a type of telemedicine service, facilitates the stroke diagnosis process by connecting emergency physicians with distant stroke neurologists within the critical window of time. Whether an urban health system offers a hub and spoke model or rural entities contract with stand-alone physician organizations for telestroke services, telestroke services increase the likelihood that someone will fully recover from a stroke.

There are many telestroke programs in the United States. You can find examples of telestroke programs by contacting the American Health Association and the American Stroke Association. Many telestroke programs have a close relationship with the tPA pharmaceutical manufacturer, Genentech.

Telestroke is one of the few telemedicine programs that require specific and reliable technology. For the most part, technology is the least important aspect of telemedicine. A variety of software and hardware can be used effectively. InTouch is the industry leader for telestroke technology and maintains an exceptional response time, as well as "up time" for its technology. Although it is very expensive, it is widely acknowledged that it is very reliable! When "time is brain," "uptime" or reliability is critical to a fast and reliable response time.

Telepsychiatry

Telepsychiatry solves persistent and recurring problems in healthcare. Namely,

•One in eight visits to the emergency department is psychiatry-related
•There is a shortage of in-patient beds
•There are 4000 health professional shortage areas
•There are only 35,000 psychiatrists, nationwide
•Telepsychiatry can improve ED throughput, result in fewer in-patient admissions.

Given these statistics, it is not surprising that telepsychiatry is the second most utilized type of telemedicine in the United States.

More than four thousand mental health professional shortage areas are identified across the United States. In many areas of the country, a patient in psychiatric crisis has only one option: the local Emergency Department.

The use of emergency room telepsychiatry benefits hospitals by supporting faster psychiatric consults, improved ED throughput, and in some areas, the ability to lift or place involuntary psychiatric holds. Therefore, telepsychiatry in the emergency department can potentially cause fewer inpatient admissions, better patient and staff satisfaction and earlier diagnosis and therapy.

The use of telepsychiatry in an outpatient setting can mean more patients getting care that is more convenient and accessible. They can obtain psychiatric services at a clinic or even in the privacy of their homes.

Low Acuity Urgent Care

Low acuity urgent care visits[15], also named video visits, eVisits, virtual visits, or tele urgent care, are defined as provider-to-consumer telemedicine service where the consumer or patient uses a computer, telephone, or mobile device to participate in a clinical consultation using a computer or device webcam, telephone or via email. A prescription or referral is often generated.

---

[15] https://www.wsj.com/articles/with-direct-primary-care-its-just-doctor-and-patient-1488164702

Retail pharmacies, like Walgreens and CVS, discovered that patients were seeking care outside of the "normal" business hours physicians were keeping. They turned their brands into healthcare centers and built facilities on nearly every corner in urban areas. They provided the consumer with an alternative to the primary care physician, urgent care provider, and emergency department visit. The pharmacies discovered that:

• 7% of adults visited the emergency room due to lack of access to other providers.
•48% went to the emergency room because the doctor's office was not open.
•43% of people do not have access to same or next-day PCP appointments.

Further, as the patient increasingly shoulders the cost of healthcare visits, they are shopping for lower cost alternatives to urgent care and the family physician.
Typically, in the United States, the average cost of primary care provider visit is $131, urgent care visit is $163, and emergency department visit is $1477.

Nontraditional healthcare providers like Teladoc, American Well, Doctor on Demand, and MD Live have developed teleurgent care services for the time-pressed and technology fluent healthcare consumer. Many of these organizations are working with healthcare population health management organizations to drive down the cost of care. Because the average telemedicine call costs $40-50, population health organizations are realizing savings of $79-1427 per visit as the telemedicine visit replaces other settings. By some estimates, teleurgent care visits are already exceeding 1.2 million annually resulting in significant savings.[16]

---

[16] http://www.hhnmag.com/articles/8350-telehealth-adoption-to-double-by-2018&

Chapter 6

Other Telemedicine Uses

Teleradiology

Teleradiology is an example of an asynchronous service that has gained popularity in the last ten years. Teleradiology is the movement of medical images, including digital x-rays, MRI, ultrasound, CT scan, and nuclear medicine studies from one site to another in order to be viewed, reviewed, interpreted, or analyzed by a radiologist.

Teleradiology programs are used by hospitals and even, radiology practices, to cover overnight radiology shifts, acquire the specialized services of subspecialty radiologists, and cover gaps in regular radiology staffing.

Teleradiology services are proving to be a revenue generator for hospitals with significant bench strength of subspecialty physicians. They are creating teleradiology programs offering the services of their subspecialty physicians to hospitals, insurance companies and other organizations that need a first or second opinion.

Tele Skilled Nursing Facility

Skilled Nursing Facilities, as well as other care settings throughout the care continuum, are investigating innovative ways to improve outcomes, reduce costs, and enhance the patient experience. Telehealth is a powerful tool to assist physicians with clinical assessment and accurate diagnosis while allowing them to extend their oversight across multiple sites.

Typically, in the skilled nursing environment, there are fewer physicians managing more patients than in a hospital setting. Nurses or medical assistants provide most of the care. They call the doctor when a change of condition occurs and offer a verbal description of the situation. A report by the Kaiser Family Foundation found that 30 to 67 percent of hospitalizations among SNF residents could be prevented with well-targeted interventions. Telehealth is one of those interventions.

Fertility

Specialists in the field of fertility may find an additional revenue stream, as well as helping patients outside of a close geographical area. Washington University Physicians proves this use case is viable.[17]

School-Based Telehealth

The Kansas University Medical Center has made significant strides in offering telemedicine services to children in rural areas. Called Telehealth ROCKS (Rural Outreach for the

---

[17] https://fertility.wustl.edu/treatments-services/telemedicine/

Children of Kansas)[18] Schools, the program offers children and school nurses a way to see family practitioners. Program providers are working with Project ECHO to gain telemedicine skills.

High Risk Maternity

An important double-blind placebo controlled study[19] using telemedicine for women with high risk pregnancies found that there were significantly better outcomes and lower costs for women using telemedicine versus the control group.

Monitoring Inpatient Outcomes in the ICU

Offsite intensivists now monitor about 10 percent of all critical care patients, and the results have been rewarding. Banner Health's eICU program has saved lives while reducing costs and preserving resources.[20] The program is run from a central operations center staffed with critical care doctors and nurses. These providers remotely monitor more than 600 ICU beds in more than 25 hospitals in seven Western states, providing welcome clinical support to hospital staff. Since launching the program, Banner Health ICUs are reporting some of the lowest ICU mortality rates in the country. In 2014, Banner Health

---

[18] http://www.kumc.edu/community-engagement/ku-center-for-telemedicine-and-telehealth/project-echo/telehealth-rocks.html

[19] https://www.ncbi.nlm.nih.gov/pubmed/11761593

[20] http://telemedicine.arizona.edu/blog/banner-health-eicu-shortens-hospital-stays-improves-patient-care

reduced predicted ICU days by 20,000, saved $68 million, and saved an estimated 2,000 lives.

Monitoring the Tiniest of Patients

Multiple health systems promote the benefits associated with tele neonatal monitoring, including positive outcomes for baby and attachment between child and parent. Utah Valley Regional Medical Center in Provo, Utah, collaborated with VSee, to support the 60-bed NICU[21]. The system provides two-way communication between physicians and parents. What's more, families can access a live stream of their baby 24/7, which helps them stay connected between visits.

Monitoring Patients with Complex Chronic Illness at Home

Studies have shown remote patient monitoring reduces unnecessary emergency department usage by 25–50 percent[22]. Several models have proven to be beneficial, including 1)Providing patients with CHF, COPD, and other chronic conditions with remote monitoring devices to track their vital signs and symptoms; 2)Care coordinators monitoring the medications and vital signs of people with limited social support; 3) Monitoring patients post-discharge to improve

[21] http://www.healthcareitnews.com/news/utah-hospital-nicu-goes-virtual-touts-telemedicine-redesign

[22] http://www.beckershospitalreview.com/healthcare-information-technology/5-top-reasons-why-remote-patient-monitoring-is-destined-to-take-off.html

outcomes, medication compliance, and reduce preventable readmissions.

This chapter lists just a few of the possible telemedicine programs and projects. Telemedicine is being used by emergency services personnel, in prisons, on oil rigs, by the military, and in catastrophic conditions. The possibilities are far-reaching and quite promising. Other types of telemedicine uses include Tele-

      Audiology

      Cardiology

      Chaplaincy

      Dentistry

      Dermatology

      Infectious disease

      Nursing

      Ophthalmology

      Pathology

      Pharmacy

      Rehabilitation

      Surgery

      Thoracic

      Trauma Care

Chapter 7

A Special Program: Project Echo

Project ECHO[23], located at the University of New Mexico, initiated by Dr. Sanjeev Arora, connects specialists in population centers with providers in areas that do not have access to medical specialists. The program is enabled by telehealth technology and endeavors to "demonopolize specialty knowledge" in medicine.

"The ECHO model® links expert specialist teams at an academic 'hub' with primary care clinicians in local communities – the 'spokes' of the model. Together, they participate in weekly teleECHO® clinics, which are like virtual grand rounds, combined with mentoring and patient case presentations. During teleECHO clinics, primary care clinicians from multiple sites present patient cases to the specialist teams and to each other, discuss new developments relating to their patients, and determine treatment. Specialists serve as mentors and colleagues, sharing their medical knowledge and expertise with primary care clinicians. Essentially, ECHO® creates ongoing learning communities where primary care clinicians receive support and develop the skills they need to treat a particular condition." (Arora, 2013)

---

[23] https://echo.unm.edu/

"Project ECHO started as a way to meet local healthcare needs. Sanjeev Arora, M.D., a liver disease doctor in Albuquerque, was frustrated that thousands of New Mexicans with hepatitis C could not get the treatment they needed because there were no specialists where they lived. The clinic where he worked was one of only two in the entire state that treated hepatitis C."

Launched in 2003, the ECHO model® makes specialized medical knowledge accessible wherever it is needed to save and improve people's lives. By putting local clinicians together with specialist teams at academic medical centers in weekly virtual clinics or teleECHO® clinics, Project ECHO shares knowledge and expands treatment capacity. The result is better care for more people.

Treatment for hepatitis C is now available at centers of excellence across New Mexico, and more than 3,000 doctors, nurses and community health workers provide treatment to more than 6,000 patients enrolled in Project ECHO's comprehensive disease management programs for myriad conditions." (Arora, 2015)

Project ECHO operates more than 50 hubs in the US, addressing more than 55 complex chronic conditions with more than 100 global partners in 22 countries.

Robert Wood Johnson, in 2009, awarded Project ECHO a prestigious, $5 million Pioneer award to expand the program and have since funded additional program expansions.

Additional Project ECHO funders include Bristol Myers Squibb, General Electric Foundation, Helmsley Charitable Trust, Con Alma Health Foundation, McCune Foundation, State of New Mexico, the Department of Defense and federal entities, AHRQ, CDC, CMS, DoD, VA, NIDA, and the NIH.

Part 3 Building a Program

Chapter 8

Creating the program structure

If you have decided that you want to embark up on or expand a telemedicine program, it is important to develop a program structure. This section will elaborate upon some of the more important aspects of building a program like developing a business plan, understanding billing, and choosing technology. Overall, telemedicine program development should include the following steps:

Build a Foundation by Creating Vision, Strategy, and Goals

First, determine your vision for the telemedicine program. What are you trying to accomplish? Are you exploring its uses? Are you trying to solve a specific problem? Are you looking for new ways to engage with patients? Is it a way to reduce overcrowding in the emergency department?

Once you have determined your vision, create a strategy for success. That strategy should include executive sponsorship, clinician support, and a budget. It could include a small pilot or a large go-live.

Establish the goals associated with the vision and the strategy. For example, do you want people to use it? How much use would be considered "project success?" On the other hand, is the goal to gather information for future deployment? As is advisable in other projects, clearly stating the vision, strategy (or mission), and goals will increase the likelihood of success. When establishing the goals, also incorporate the metrics that will be used to measure progress.

Expand the Foundation with Budget, Governance, Reporting

Make a financial commitment to the program's success, at least during the pilot phase. Without a budget, your telemedicine project will be a secondary research endeavor only.

Once you have determined your vision, created your strategy, established measurable goals, and made a financial commitment, decide the type of telemedicine that is in alignment with these factors. NOTE: Some people start with a telemedicine solution first, but it is more likely to be successful if you set a vision, strategy, goals and budget prior to choosing the telemedicine solution.

Governance is an important aspect of program success. Formal healthcare systems have committees and forums to facilitate communication and to develop a consensus of support among leadership. Any organization that is attempting to launch telemedicine, even if formal governance avenues do not exist, should consider creating an informal cross-functional committee of leaders to facilitate the success of the project. Telemedicine's complexity necessitates that every aspect of the organization will be touched. Having a leadership team committed to the program's success is valuable and necessary for long-term success.

Consistently reporting the operational status and the metrics that are measuring its success keeps the project on track and takes the subjectivity out of the program's progress.

Choosing a Platform

Once a foundation has been built, take the time to choose a software platform and vendor with whom you can collaborate for the long term. A partnership with a vendor will contribute to a successful project. Excellent and comprehensive telemedicine software tools already exist. Do not develop a custom platform. It is a costly venture that requires long-term maintenance. Unless software development is a core competency of the organization, select a software vendor.

Create a pilot plan that limits the number of clinicians that need to be trained. Creating a successful pilot means choosing participants (including people and staff) who are flexible, open-minded, and cooperative. Ideally, they are also communicative and have a positive attitude towards innovation.

Set a go-live date and work towards that date by building your operational plans to include checklists, workflows, and data flows in conjunction with the impacted department (e.g. emergency department, surgical suite, primary care physician's office.)

Pilot Plan with Communications and Training

Develop an internal communications plan and execute. Ensure that all constituents, including the information technology department, administration, risk, quality, legal, and medical leadership are apprised of the plan and support its success.

Develop an external communications plan. Communicating with patients can be complex. Using tools like the Flesch Kincaid tool embedded into Microsoft Word can assist with writing text applicable to a diverse patient population. Communicating with patients usually means describing the encounter, explaining the way it works, gaining their agreement to participate, and allaying any fears about privacy. Telemedicine typically does not need the complex "consenting" associated with human trials but reviewing those guidelines can positively inform the communications.

Conduct training for all participants in the telemedicine pilot. Specifically, focus on the providers and staff that will be the "boots on the ground." At the elbow training combined with job aids, workflow lists, and screen captures will improve the likelihood of success.

The day before go-live, test the equipment, notify everyone that will be impacted and be present for last minute questions and issues.

Build an Enduring Program Infrastructure

Once you have completed a pilot program, assess its success using the measures that have been established. Working with your sponsors and key constituents, decide if you would like to expand the program, try a different project or scrap it.

If you decide to expand the program, begin to build the infrastructure for scaling the operation. Inserting telemedicine into the organization involves establishing billing guidelines. (See Chapter 10)

Collaborating with the risk, legal and regulatory teams is important (see Chapter 12) since they will help to ensure compliance, as well as protecting the organization from privacy leaks. This group often can assist with policy writing, as well.

Establishing an IT infrastructure including technology standards and data storage and transfer requirements is important so that the telemedicine program projects are seamlessly exchanging data. Addressing the data transfers between EHRs and health information exchanges (HIEs) is also important.

Lastly, ensure there are clinical and operational workflow guidelines that closely integrate the existing operations with the new telemedicine services. Staffing should be scheduled and all applicable staff, adequately trained in the operational procedures, as well as the consenting, data flows and technology support services.

Chapter 9

Developing a Business Case

Telemedicine is not simply a revenue-generating tool. In fact, sometimes its most important value propositions do not generate revenue. Below are the viable financial models associated with telehealth. They include:

Cost Avoidance for "Capitated or At-Risk" Patients

When an organization is "at risk" for the overall cost of care associated with a population's health, it is important that the patient uses the most cost-effective approach to seek care. Therefore, redirecting an allergy-suffering patient from the emergency department on the weekends to a telemedicine option with distant providers would result in a significant savings to the patient and the hospital.

Cost Reduction

Physicians, and especially specialists, are an expensive resource. The use of telemedicine extends these precious resources to additional hospitals by relieving physicians from unnecessary travel. It also offers the physician at home the ability to see home bound or skilled nursing patients as needed instead of unnecessary trips to facilities.

Reduce Length of Stay in the Acute Setting

Hospitalized patients spend most of their time waiting to see physicians in order to be examined or for tests to be ordered. Telemedicine can bring the physicians to the bedside more swiftly so that tests can be ordered and results reviewed. There is the potential for length of stay to be reduced. In addition, continuous monitoring of patients in the intensive care unit and neonatal units has proven to reduce the length of hospitalization and provide patients with additional care coverage.

Reduce Readmissions

Monitoring patients at home or in a skilled nursing facility, especially those patients with complex chronic conditions can reduce readmissions. Patients and facilities are less likely to arrive back in the emergency department to see a physician "just in case it's serious."

Direct Revenue Generation

Organizations can use telemedicine to expand their opportunities to generate revenue. For example, they can offer specialist services to rural entities. They can expand their services beyond their geography. They can extend services into the jails, schools, communities, and individuals.

New Business Models

There are many areas in healthcare where people are willing to pay cash for consultations for example, fertility consultations, genetic consulting, and plastic surgery consultations. A viable, revenue generating telemedicine business can be created worldwide if there are people who are willing to pay for the encounter. Specialists with excellent reputations can develop another revenue source using telemedicine.

Second Opinion Services

Johns Hopkins[24] and Barrow Brain and Spine[25] are using telemedicine to offer second opinions. Patients send their scans, medical records, and physician opinions to specialists who are skilled at assessing specific conditions. If the physicians believe they can assist the patient, they contact the patient and offer their services. It is a way for a powerful organization to extend their brand and for patients to consult with prominent specialists.

---

[24] http://www.hopkinsmedicine.org/second_opinion/index.html
[25] https://www.barrowbrainandspine.com/the-patient-experience/second-opinion/

Examples of Telemedicine Uses

Type of Telemedicine service	Type of telemedicine service	Setting	Synchronous /Asynchronous	Value Proposition
ICU / NICU monitoring	Continuous Monitoring or Provider to Consumer	Acute	S	Anticipate adverse events, higher level of care, reduction in lengths of stay, patient satisfaction
Telestroke Networks, Behavioral Health	Provider to provider to consumer	Acute, Ambulatory	S	Balance workforce, provide specialists to rural areas
Dermatology, Pathology	Provider to provider	Acute or Ambulatory	A	Convenience
Internal medicine doctor discusses case with cardiologist	Provider to provider consults	Acute or Ambulatory	S	Medical Home Model, better quality of care, supports continuum of care
Tumor Boards, Grand Rounds, Project Echo	Medical Education	Acute or Ambulatory	S, A	Knowledge transfer, professional education
Chronic Complex patient visits	Provider to existing patient	Ambulatory	S	Patient convenience, closer monitoring of care
Various companies including Teladoc, American	Provider to new patient (on demand)	Ambulatory, Occupational Health	S	Cost avoidance

Well, Doctor on Demand				
Post-Discharge CHF patients monitored	Home monitoring	Ambulatory	S	Cost avoidance, pop health management
Radiology images read by radiologists	Image Sharing	Acute and Ambulatory	A	Revenue Generation

Chapter 10

Is Your Telemedicine Encounter Billable?

Although recent improvements have been made, the reimbursement for telehealth services has been complex. It is dependent upon the payer source, the type of telehealth interaction, patient geography, special coding, and a host of other dependencies.

Each payer source, Medicare, Medicaid, and Private Payers, has different definitions and parameters for billing. They delineate and define key elements associated with billing guidelines. Referring to their guiding policy is critical to determining their unique criteria. Sometimes, it can be a challenge to find the most current policy. For example, Medicare has eight different source documents that guide telehealth billing.

Regardless, there IS a way to be paid for telemedicine! Following these steps will assist you in assessing whether or not your telemedicine encounter may be billable. This is only a guide. Check with your private payer, Medicare or Medicaid technical expert and organization billing staff to verify!

1. Identify the Payer

Broadly speaking, it will likely be Medicare, Medicaid or a private payer. There are many permutations, including the Medicare Advantage payers, the accountable care organizations, health maintenance organizations, etc. but for simple demonstration purposes, assume there are only three buckets.

2. Determine the Five Factors Associated with Reimbursement including:

a. What is the type of telehealth transaction?

Synchronous: If the transaction is synchronous or occurring at the same time, like a video conferencing application, it is quite possibly billable. Synchronous interactions require webcam use.

Asynchronous: If the transaction is a scan, photo, or some other type of static document captured and then sent to a provider for review later, it is considered an "asynchronous" or "Store and Forward" telemedicine transaction. There are a few states, namely Alaska and Hawaii, where Medicare will reimburse for these expenses. Nevertheless, for the most part, they are unbillable.

Monitoring: Remote monitoring is billable as a remote or ambulatory service with code 99490. It is not yet billable in the acute environment.

b. Is there a geographic or rural requirement?
Most payers apply a geographic restriction or definition to the telemedicine encounter in order to allow billing for services. Medicare defines as "rural" as a non-Metropolitan Statistical Area or Health Professional Shortage Area[26]

c. Where is the telemedicine encounter initiated or "site-type?"
Qualified site-types vary depending upon the payer. For Medicare, the qualified sites to initiate or receive billable telemedicine encounters are Physician or provider office, Hospitals, Critical Access Hospitals, Rural Health Clinics, Federally Qualified Health Centers, Hospital-based or CAH-based Renal Dialysis Centers (including satellites), Skilled Nursing Facilities (SNF), and Community Mental Health Centers.

d. Who is the practitioner and are they deemed eligible?
The eligible practitioner type also varies depending upon the payer. For Medicare, the eligible practitioners allowed to bill for telemedicine encounters are Physicians, Nurse Practitioners, Physician Assistants, Nurse Midwives, Clinical

---

[26] https://datawarehouse.hrsa.gov/tools/analyzers/hpsafind.aspx

Nurse Specialists (CNS), Clinical Psychologists, and Clinical Social Workers.

e. Does the coding accurately reflect the telemedicine encounter?

When submitting a bill to Medicare, Medicaid, or Private Payers, the coding should be the same as a non-telemedicine encounter. The difference is the coding. Coders should add GT or GQ modifiers to the code number. There are some providers who choose not to do so but this practice runs the risk of audit irregularities that could result in fines.

Remote patient monitoring is different. There are specific separate codes that can be billed for remote patient monitoring but it is an ever-evolving area of CMS guidance so check out CMS. 99490 and additional codes can be your friend!

f. State by State variations

Varying from state to state, other aspects affect the telemedicine encounter including whether or not a telemedicine coordinator is present and if a physician relationship was established by an in-person encounter.

Key element	Medicare	Medicaid*	Private Payers
Definition of telehealth	An **interactive audio and video** telecommunications system must be used that permits **real-time communication** between you, at the distant site, and the beneficiary, at the originating site. **Asynchronous "store and forward"** technology is **not permitted** (except for demonstration programs.)	Different states vary. For example, in Arizona, both asynchronous and synchronous services are billable.	Nearly every private payer uses Medicare's definition or a very similar one.
Rural designation required by originating site?	Yes	Varies	Varies
Rural Definition	HPSA, non-MSA, Rural census tract as determined by Office of Rural Health Policy within HRSA (website available for determination: http://datawarehouse.hrsa.gov/ telehealthAdvisor/telehealthEligibility.aspx	Varies	Varies
Eligible originating facility site	1. Physician or provider office 2. Hospitals 3. Critical Access Hospitals 4. Rural Health Clinics 5. Federally Qualified Health Centers 6. Hospital-based or CAH-based Renal Dialysis Centers (including satellites) 7. Skilled Nursing Facilities (SNF); 8. Community Mental Health Centers	Varies by State: As an example, AZ includes: 1. IHS clinic 2. Tribally-governed 638 facility 3. Urban clinic for Native Americans 4. Office of a	Nearly every private payer uses Medicare's definition or a very similar one.

			physician or other practitioner 5. *Hospital* 6. *Federally qualified health center (FQHC)*	
Eligible distant site practitioners	1. Physicians 2. Nurse Practitioners 3. Physician Assistants 4. Nurse Midwives 5. Clinical nurse specialists (CNS) 6. Clinical psychologists and clinical social workers	Varies	Often, providers who are members of their network.
Covered Specialties	See Rural health Fact Sheer Series (ICM 901705, April 2014)	Varies	Varies but is often more restrictive than Medicare.
Other	1. Distant sites are paid the provider fee. 2. Originating sites are paid an originating site facility fee ONLY (HCPCS Code Q3014.)	Varies but often does NOT pay originating site fee	Unknown

Chapter 11

Technology and data integration

Technology vendors often drive telemedicine projects. Significant technology innovations will continue to change the landscape of telemedicine and medical care delivery. That said, at some point, technology must be selected to support the program's operations. Technology is critical to ensuring a successful launch and, ultimately affects your ability to scale the program.

Choosing a technology vendor should be initiated with a survey of applicable vendors. Usually, sending a request for information (RFI) to many vendors will serve that purpose. After reviewing the RFI responses, select the top four vendors to send a Request for Proposal (RFP) with all of the detailed questions required by the sponsors and constituents previously identified. Using a score sheet and checking references keeps the process logical, fair, and thorough.

Software Options

Software can range dramatically from custom solutions, proprietary systems, or a HIPAA compliant video technology. Below is a partial but certainly not exhaustive list of potential vendors in each space.

Type of Program	Care Setting 1	Care Setting 2	Potential Technology Vendors
Intensive Care Unit Monitoring	Hospital	NA	**Philips**[27], **Advanced ICU**[28] **Care**
Telestroke	Hospital	Community Hospital	**InTouch Health**[29], **Reach Health**[30], Other niche providers; sometimes the telemedicine stroke providers, like **Specialists on Call**[31] will offer a custom solution
Telepsychiatry	Hospital	Clinic	**VSee**[32], **eVisit**[33], **Cloud Visit**[34], **TruClinic**[35], **American Well**[36], and a wide range of simple solutions like Zoom.
Teleurgent Care	Clinic	Home	Wide range including American Well, **Doctor on Demand**[37], **MD Live**[38], **Teladoc**[39], TruClinic, **Zoom**[40]

---

[27] http://www.usa.philips.com/healthcare/product/HCNOCTN503/eicu-program-telehealth-for-the-intensive-care-unit

[28] http://www.advancedicucare.com/

[29] https://www.intouchhealth.com/

[30] https://reachhealth.com/

[31] http://specialistsoncall.com/

[32] https://www.vsee.com

[33] https://evisit.com/

[34] https://www.cloudvisittm.com/

[35] https://www.truclinic.com/

[36] https://www.americanwell.com/

[37] https://www.doctorondemand.com/

Hardware Device options

Various hardware solutions can be used to enable telemedicine encounters. For the purposes of this section, we are not covering intensive care monitoring.

Telemedicine Carts

For specialized care that requires precision and cleanliness, a medical grade telemedicine cart can be purchased for several thousand dollars. A cart enables peripherals to be added that can enhance the examination. Telemedicine cart strengths as a tool includes medical-grade quality, ability to be cleaned, security, and additional peripherals tools to enhance examinations, like otoscopes, stethoscopes, and heart monitors. Telemedicine cart disadvantages are cost, floor space, and storage. Two leading telemedicine cart vendors are Avizia[41] and Global Med[42].

Tablet With or Without a Stand

Tablets can be purchased for hundreds of dollars, making it an affordable solution, especially for the skilled nursing or home setting. Tablet advantages are that it is inexpensive, requires

---

[38] https://www.mdlive.com/

[39] https://www.teladoc.com

[40] https://zoom.us/healthcare

[41] https://www.avizia.com/

[42] https://www.globalmed.com/

little training, and are portable. The tablet's disadvantages are that it can be difficult to locate, can be easily "borrowed," is difficult to clean, and offers few medical grade peripherals.

Laptop Computer with Web or Video Camera
A simple laptop computer with a web or video camera can be used to power telemedicine. Acquiring a computer costs more than a tablet but significantly less than telemedicine cart. The advantages of a laptop computer are that it is inexpensive and people already know how to use it. The disadvantages are that the computer can "walk away," is difficult to clean, and offers few medical grade peripherals.

Data Integration

Telemedicine is unlikely to become integrated into the core operations of an organization until the data can easily flow to and from existing data sources. Every organization's data is handled differently. Some have a health information exchange, others have a proprietary data mart, and others have large data warehouses. Telemedicine encounters should be integrated into the electronic health record. Avoid the temptation to store the data in a "one-off" location. Some EHR software companies are incorporating telemedicine into their platform.

Tap into the expertise of your technology teams. They will appreciate your questions about data formatting. As you identify the data and its flow, members of data team can offer guidance about the HL7 or Consolidated Clinical Document Architecture (CCDA) standards and will help you create a data plan. Include the data scientists, communication experts, and network engineers in the telemedicine project. They add value and offer a broad perspective.

Chapter 12

Telemedicine Staffing

As telemedicine grows, there is a need for professionals to create, run, and work within the telemedicine programs. There is little agreement about how to "rank" or name telemedicine program positions. Job titles include telehealth coordinator, telemedicine program director, telemedicine program manager, and telehealth senior manager, to name a few. One study showed nearly 30 different titles for roughly the same job. Below are common jobs associated with telemedicine programs. Because the field is not yet mature, program are staffed with people who may be entering from other fields. Consequently, each category includes a descriptor, as well as important skills professionals may wish to acquire should they wish to be considered for roles in successful in telemedicine programs.

Clinical

Clinical positions include nurses, physicians, nurse practitioners, and physician assistants. Increasingly, some programs, like the continuous monitoring programs are use nursing assistants or medical technicians. If you are currently a clinician and would like to work in the field, look for opportunities to participate in pilot programs or introduce telemedicine into your organization. Across the country, there are excellent certificate and degree programs emphasizing clinical informatics.

The key to embarking upon telemedicine as a clinician is to show an interest in the field. Read about it. Subscribe to the mailing lists detailed in the appendix. In addition, learn about technology. Often, nurses and physicians understand some core medical systems but may not be as facile with different types of technology. Learn how to use the various workstations on wheels, iPads, computers, and electronic medical records. If you are a physician, there are services you can register to appear as an on-call physician. With little commitment, except to show up to your shift, you can experiment with different services especially in the low acuity urgent care space. If you are a psychiatrist or psychologist, there are services that will welcome you. Some of the services to investigate include Doctor on Demand, Teladoc, American Well, MD Live, TruClinic, MeMD[43], and others.

Technology

Sometimes telemedicine programs rest in the information technology (IT) department. This practice is not advisable, as the mission of most IT departments in healthcare organizations is to keep the organization secure. Developing innovative projects and programs that open the organization to new technologies, processes, and data directly opposes the

---

[43] https://www.memd.com

mission. By its very nature, healthcare innovation, including telemedicine challenges the status quo. That said, at some point telemedicine programs will likely encounter the IT department, even if they are not located in that department.

Telemedicine positions that may reside in the IT department are program manager positions, data engineering positions, and telemedicine coordinator positions. If you are located in the IT department and wish to embark upon telemedicine, begin to learn about it, sit on the technology selection committee, and understand the interaction between IT and the clinical team that is using telemedicine. There is a strong need for people to understand BOTH the clinical aspects of telemedicine and the technology required to operate it. Ideally, once both aspects are understood, a valuable professional would be able to effectively communicate the concepts and serve as a liaison between the disparate teams.

Project Management

All telemedicine projects require project management. Learning the key principles of project management and then applying them to telemedicine projects is another way to enter the field. Telemedicine projects can be approached like other information technology projects. They are complex projects with multiple elements and a variety of stakeholders.

Program Management

Most telemedicine programs require a person who understands all aspects of the telemedicine proposition. Program management requires an understanding of the financial, legal, technological, and clinical aspects of telemedicine. It does not require a clinical degree but often program managers are nurses who have obtained additional training in project management, informatics, or technology.

Administration

An operations executive assigned that task by senior leadership may initiate some telemedicine programs. Once the program is initiated, the program adds personnel, like program managers, clinicians, and technologists. Healthcare executives and administrators assigned this role are in a unique position to build a career in telemedicine and run even larger telemedicine operations. Whether or not an administrator is assigned a formal role, it is important to identify an administrator to help champion the project. Both a physician leader and an administrator/leader as sponsors will facilitate program success.

Chapter 13

Other Operational Considerations

Training

Training for the clinicians that will be conducting telemedicine encounters is critical. The training should include not just the physicians but also the scribes, medical assistants, nurses and other personnel that will be "touching" the system. The physician may be on the screen but getting the system setup and positioned correctly requires other personnel.

Communications

As a best practice, all stakeholders affected by the telemedicine project should be apprised of the project. Patients, the quality team, administrators, leaders, nurses, and staff may all be impacted. Having a consistent and concise message about the vision, impact, benefits, and operational details is critical to project success.

Risk

Every healthcare organization has a risk management department. Conferring with that team is advisable in the event that there are precautions that must be taken to reduce any potential negative impact.

Workflows

Creating a flow chart of the telemedicine encounter is a valuable tool to share with staff. It gives everyone an overview of the entire process and allows him or her to digest and comment on the operational steps. Presenting the workflows during training gives staff the opportunity to identify any items that may have been missed in the workflow development.

Printed Guides or Job Aids

Creating a paper job aid that can sit with the equipment or in the pocket of a provider is a valuable tool for providers and staff. Until the telemedicine processes and methods become incorporated into their every day job tasks, there is a learning curve. Having a printed job aid or guide supports the new processes and supports the change management goals.

Part 4 Laws, Regulations, and Policy

Chapter 14

Laws and Regulations

Perhaps the most complex issues associated with telehealth are the legal issues. A thorough understanding of the legal and regulatory issues associated with telehealth is critical to successful deployment. Below are common issues and resources that are important to address as you grow telemedicine within your organization. NOTE: The author is not an attorney. This information should be used for guidance and research purposes only. Seek professional legal services by licensed professionals.

Malpractice insurance

Organizations should understand and review the physician or provider malpractice limits and requirements of their coverage as it pertains to telemedicine. If a telemedicine program includes patient visits in non-specified locations, there is a potential for malpractice coverage being inapplicable. Without licensure in the patient's location (State or Country), the physician, or provider risks practicing medicine without a license. Most professional liability insurance policies specifically exclude coverage for unlicensed activities; some states require professional liability underwriters to cover practice that extends beyond state borders and some do not.

Privacy of patient data and health information

Address the organization's expectations around the applicable federal and state legal requirements of medical/health information privacy, including compliance with the Health Insurance Portability and Accountability Act (HIPAA) and state privacy, confidentiality, security, and medical retention rules. Some organizations refer physicians to "Standards for Privacy of Individually Identifiable Health Information," issued by the Department of Health and Human Services (HHS)[44].

Jurisdiction

Because laws vary from state to state, organizations should specify the policies' ruling jurisdiction. Most policies are subject to the laws, statutes, and regulations of a particular state, the Centers for Medicaid and Medicare, and any other applicable or over riding legal entities. You may want to add a disclaimer that due to the fluid and changing nature of telemedicine, the most current laws, statutes, and regulations apply.

Licensure

The location of the patient when the telemedicine encounter occurs is the determining factor for physician or provider

---

[44] https://aspe.hhs.gov/standards-privacy-individually-identifiable-health-information

licensure. In other words, the practice of telemedicine occurs where the patient is located when the telemedicine technologies are used. Therefore, a physician or provider must be licensed by, or be under the jurisdiction of, the medical board of the state where the patient is located. Physicians or providers who treat or prescribe via telemedicine are practicing medicine and must possess appropriate licensure in all jurisdictions where patients receive care. HRSA provided a comprehensive review of licensure with specific attention paid to telehealth with its Senate report 111-66[45].

---

[45] https://www.congress.gov/congressional-report/111th-congress/senate-report/66

Chapter 15

Interstate Licensure Compact

Telehealth services require that the physician be licensed in the state where the patient is physically located. Because each individual state licenses its physicians and besides the veteran's administration, there is no federal mechanism to license physicians, the question of license portability is being investigated. A medical licensure compact for physicians is in process. A nursing compact already exists.

Telemedicine currently requires physicians become licensed in each state where they are practicing medicine. Technology is changing the definition of an "exam." It is enabling physicians to examine, diagnose, and treat a patient without regard to geography. Physicians wishing to practice in multiple states must become licensed in each state where patients may reside. Multi-state licensure therefore becomes expensive and burdensome for physicians practicing telemedicine.

Nurses are able to use their licenses across states via reciprocity and a multi-state compact that eases the burden of licensure and enhances license portability.

In 2013, a number of state medical boards, the Federation of State Medical Boards[46], and experts from the Council of State Governments, and interested stakeholder groups began to explore forming an interstate compact for physicians. Eighteen months later, a compact was drafted that is being contemplated by physicians, state medical boards, and state legislatures.

Below are the eight consensus principles quoted directly from the FSMB website. They include:

•Participation in an interstate compact for medical licensure will be strictly voluntary for both physicians and state boards of medicine.

•Participation in an interstate compact creates another pathway for licensure, but does not otherwise change a state's existing Medical Practice Act.

•The practice of medicine occurs where the patient is located at the time of the physician-patient encounter, and therefore, requires the physician to be under the jurisdiction of the state medical board where the patient is located.

•An interstate compact for medical licensure will establish a mechanism whereby any physician practicing in the state will

---

[46] https://www.fsmb.org/

be known by, and under the jurisdiction of, the state medical board where the practice occurs.

•Regulatory authority will remain with the participating state medical boards and will not be delegated to any entity that would administer a compact.

•A physician practicing under an interstate compact is bound to comply with the statutes, rules and regulations of each compact state wherein he / she chooses to practice.

•State boards participating in an interstate compact are required to share complaint / investigative information with each other.

•The license to practice can be revoked by any or all of the compact states.

Currently, state legislatures and medical boards are considering draft legislation to participate in the Interstate Medical Licensure Compact[47]. To date, 22 states have joined the compact.

---

[47] http://www.imlcc.org/

Chapter 16

Policy

It is beneficial for healthcare organizations to create telemedicine policies that are consistent and aligned with existing policies. If telemedicine is treated as a "one-off" or unique program, the likelihood it growing to the enterprise level is very low. Policies provide guidance about establishing professional medical practices while using telemedicine technologies. They define the standards of care and interactions both in the delivery of medical services directly to patients and between clinicians while using telemedicine technologies.

Clearly delineating clinical, documentation and quality standards will increase the likelihood sustaining successful telemedicine encounters. The use of technology can wedge a gap between patient and provider. As such, it is important in policy to encourage providers to use communication tools and approaches that bridge the natural gap that occurs during the use of technology.

While writing policies about telemedicine, it is important to define the types of telemedicine that are included and those that are excluded. For example, telemedicine policies may include or exclude audio-only telephony, routine e-mail, instant messaging, and fax. Define the terms of telemedicine so that it addresses synchronous, asynchronous, and continuous monitoring. Important elements of policies may include:

Consent

Many hospitals or providers have incorporated telemedicine into their general consent forms but if your organization has not, it is worth considering a consent form presented to the patient at the time of the telemedicine encounter.

Physicians and Prescribing

When pharmaceuticals are prescribed during the telemedicine encounter, policies that address patient safety in the absence of a traditional physical examination are advisable. Policies should include measures to guarantee the identity of the patient, to establish a patient/provider relationship, and to create detailed documentation for the clinical evaluation and resulting prescription. Record retention policies should reflect organizational standards. Note: It is illegal to prescribe controlled substances using telemedicine.

Policies should delineate that physicians or providers should not establish or maintain preferred relationships with any pharmacy. There should not be an exchange of consideration, benefit or any type of remuneration for transmitting prescriptions to or recommending a pharmacy.

Credentialing

Hospitals sometimes require that physicians and providers performing telemedicine services be credentialed according to the medical staff by-laws, policies, and procedures. In particular, credentialing is an important consideration for hospital based telemedicine activities. Some hospitals offer expedited and abbreviated credentialing if the physician will not see patients on the hospital premises. Consult with the medical staff services to develop policies that are consistent with the organization's existing policies.

Privileging

Some hospitals require that any physician/provider providing telemedicine services on their behalf must apply for and maintain privileges according to their employing or contracting entity's processes and standards. They will often reference the medical staff bylaws, policies and procedures, as well as Medicare requirements.

Documentation

A telemedicine encounter is a medical encounter. If a patient medical record already exists, it is important to document the encounter. If there is not a pre-existing patient record, it is recommended that a medical record be created for all telemedicine patients, whether or not one already exists. The record should specify that the visit has occurred via telemedicine.

Final Thoughts

Telemedicine is poised to double in the next two years. Every area of telemedicine has exponential growth potential. Yet, treating telemedicine as an important new care delivery method instead of a "one-off" pilot project will ensure its long-term success. Developing a comprehensive program infrastructure similar to that associated with traditional care will increase the likelihood of enterprise adoption and growth. Although implementing telemedicine is complex and challenging, it is well worth the effort to bring care to patients who need a different type of healthcare setting.

As healthcare professionals work to achieve the "Triple Aim" of better healthcare, lower costs, and improved population health, telemedicine is a valuable tool. As technology continues to improve telemedicine may incorporate virtual reality, augmented reality, predictive data analytics, and improved technology such that anywhere someone has access to the internet, a person will have access to medical care.

APPENDIX

Organizations to Join

•American Telemedicine Association:
https://www.americantelemed.org
•HIMSS: Health Information and Management Systems
Society- http://www.himss.org
•AHIMA: American Health Information Management
Association- https://www.ahima.org
•cTel: Center for Telehealth and e-Health Law:
https://www.ctel.org

•Regional Telehealth Centers are a system of telehealth
regional resource centers assisting the rural entities. They
offer excellent resources. They do not offer funding but do
provide technical assistance, consulting, and matchmaking
between physicians, vendors, and health organizations.

•Find your resource center at the map at
https://www.telehealthresourcecenter.org/who-your-trc

- Northwest Regional Telehealth Resource Center:
  https://www.nrtrc.org
- California Telehealth Resource Center:
  https://www.caltrc.org

- Southwest Telehealth Resource Center: https://www.southwesttrc.org
- Great Plain Telehealth Resources and Assistance Center: https://www.gptrac.org
- Heartland Telehealth Resource Center: https://www.heartlandtrc.org
- TEXLA Telehealth Resource Center: https://www.textlatrc.org
- Northeast Telehealth Resource Center: https://www.netrc.org
- Upper Midwest Telehealth Resource Center: https://www.umtrc.org
- MidAtlantic Telehealth Resource Center: https://www.matrc.org
- South Central Telehealth Resource Center: https://www.learntelehealth.org
- Southeastern Telehealth Resource Center: https://www.gatelehealth.org

Subscribe to these Mailing Lists

•Center for Connected Health Policy:
http://www.cchpca.org/subscribe

•cTel: http://www.ctel.org/newsletter/

•Federal Telemedicine News:
https://www.federaltelemedicine.com/?page_id=124

•Fierce IT: https://fiercehealthcare.com/it

•Gartner: https://www.gartner.com

•Health Affairs: https://www.healthaffairs.org

•Healthcare Dive: https://www.healthcaredive.com

•Healthcare Law Today:
https://www.healthcarelawtoday.com

•National Academy Press: https://www.nap.edu

•ONC Health IT: https://www.healthit.gov

•Rock Weekly: https://rockhealth.com/rock-weekly/

•Tractica Advisory: https://www.tractica.com

Resource Links

Billing

•Eligibility link at HRSA:
http://datawarehouse.hrsa.goc/tools/analyzers/geo/Telehealth.aspx
•Link to CMS ruling: http://www.cms.gov

Accreditation

•American Telemedicine Association:
 http://www.americantelemed.org/ata-accreditation
•URAC: https://www.urac.org/about-urac/about-urac/
•The Joint Commission: https://www.jointcommission.org

Policy and Legislation

•Telehealth Medicaid and State Policy and Interactive Map:
http://www.cchpca.org/telehealth-medicaid-state-policy
•State Telemedicine Gaps Report:
 http://www.americantelemed.org/policy-page/state-
telemedicine-gaps-reports
•Privacy and policy documents at the HHS Office for Civil
Rights Web site: www.hhs.gov/ocr/hipaa

Legal Resources

•A 50-State Survey of Telehealth legalities is found at the American Health Lawyers Association (AHLA) site. http://www.healthlawyers.org/store/Pages/Product-Details.aspx?productid={FE8568A5-DCDC-E611-9419-0050569E348F} There is a fee but it is an excellent resource

•Epstein Becker Green Telemental/Telebehavioral Health 50-state Survey: https://e-coms.ebglaw.com/61/260/landing-pages/thank-you---accept.asp

•State Laws and Reimbursement Policies: http://www.cchpca.org/state-laws-and-reimbursement-policies

•Licensure gap analysis: A 50-state gap analysis associated with physician practice standards and licensure is found at the American Telemedicine Association site.

•Credentialing and Privileging: Credentialing and privileging is a challenging issue for telehealth practitioners and the organizations that wish to use them. CMS issued a final rule in July, 2011. http://www.gpo.gov/fdsys/pkg/FR-2011-05-05/pdf/2011-10875.pdf

•And cTel provides an analysis and explanation at
http://ctel.org/expertise/credentialing-and-privileging/

Trends to Watch

•Medicare Billing:
https://www.cms.gov/medicare/medicare-general-information/telehealth/

•Interstate licensure Compact: https://www.imlcc.org

•Federation of State Medical Boards (Compact):
https://www.fsmb.org/Media/Default/PDF/Advocacy/Interstate%20Medical%20Licensure%20Compact%20(FINAL).pdf

Biography

Andrea Kamenca was accepted into Claremont McKenna College as a Tuohy scholar. She completed her degree at the University of Maryland, European Division where she graduated with honors. She then began her career in pharmaceutical sales. Admitted into the University of Southern California as a Simonsen Fellow, she completed a Master of Business Administration. Andrea then went to work in field of technology working for PriceWaterhouseCoopers, a Microsoft partner, and IBM.

She then shifted gears and embarked onto a career path in marketing and business development, where she founded and owned a business ranked in the top 7% of small businesses in the United States.

After selling her business, Andrea accepted an offer to direct healthcare operations at a public health clinic. After receiving an Office of the National Coordinator scholarship to attend the University of Colorado, Denver, she completed a post-graduate certificate in healthcare informatics. Andrea then spent the next four years implementing various types of telemedicine for large organizations at multiple sites.

58058587R00051

Made in the USA
Middletown, DE
04 August 2019